FOR THE COLORFUL TEACHER

by Karen Campbell & Kris Taft Miller

Because teachers are people too!

Wordsmith Genius: Tara Podvojsky

Karen Campbell
www.karencampbellartist.com
Kris Taft Miller
www.printdesignsbykris.com

DEDICATIONS

• From Karen •

This book is dedicated to all the AMAZING teachers in the world out there. We will never ever fully understand how on earth you do what you do every day, but we are eternally grateful that you do. To Sean, Jack, Billy and Max, I am grateful everyday for your collective extreme handsomeness and awesomeness, I am one lucky wife and mama!! I'd also like to thank my creative sister from another mister, Kris Miller!!! Without whom I wouldn't be an author at all.

• From Kris •

To all of the amazing teachers out there, you know who you are, what would we do without you? And to Karen Campbell, how did we get so lucky as to stumble into each other in life?!
Finally, to my three boys, my amazing sons Charlie and James who keep me laughing and inspired every day and my husband, Jeremy, you are my person.

FIRST I DRINK THE COFFEE...

Decorate your coffee cup with whatever helps you get through the day.

Welcome to
TEACHING!
Where the salaries are low and everything is your fault!

HOW ARE YOUR NERVES?

Draw these shapes at the beginning of the school year and at the end of the school year to see how your nerves hold up.

circle

circle

square

square

rectangle

rectangle

MYSTERY SPILL COLOR-BY-NUMBER

Color in the mystery spills using the color key provided.
Can you guess the identity of the unknown fluids?

1. Red
2. Brown
3. Pink
4. White
5. Purple
6. Green
7. Yellow

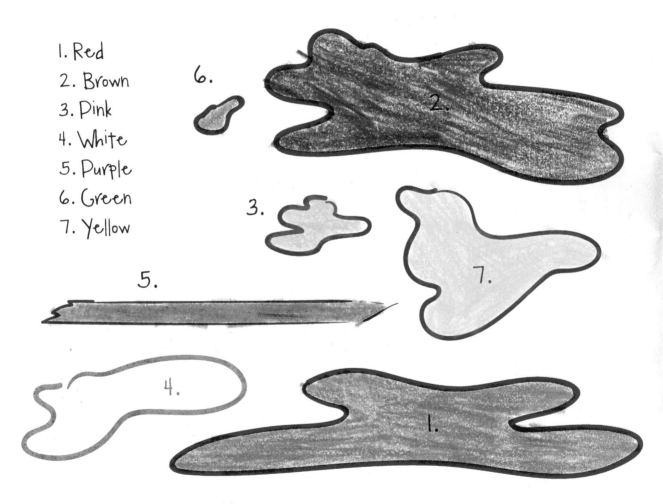

Answers on page 95.

WORKING FOR THE WEEKEND!

S	K	O	O	B	E	R	O	M	O	N	M
A	A	K	N	A	R	H	A	N	B	C	X
W	M	U	J	N	O	A	L	A	R	M	F
E	J	T	Q	C	M	P	R	X	I	I	U
W	T	N	Z	Q	E	P	E	R	G	Q	M
E	M	I	T	G	N	I	T	T	I	U	Q
E	F	Y	W	F	O	N	X	A	L	R	T
K	I	D	F	R	E	E	Z	O	N	E	S
E	X	Y	U	E	M	S	U	N	D	A	Y
N	D	Y	N	E	R	S	T	H	T	W	S
D	U	J	D	D	U	G	Z	U	U	T	H
S	O	F	A	O	O	Y	R	Y	A	I	Y
Y	Y	I	Y	M	P	D	V	O	F	J	P
H	I	C	O	Y	R	V	W	T	U	O	W

enjoy
freedom
funday
happiness
kid free zone
no alarm
no more books
pour me one more
quitting time
relaxation
saturday
sunday
tgif
weekends
sofa

99 GLASSES OF WINE ON THE WALL

Color in a glass every time you pour yourself some much needed wine...your first week back.

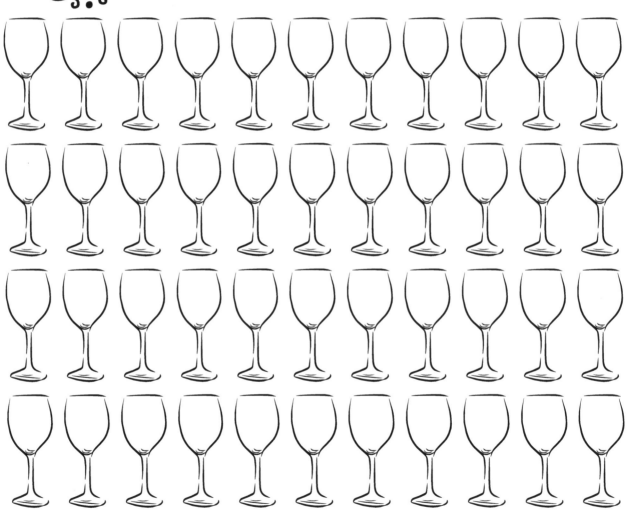

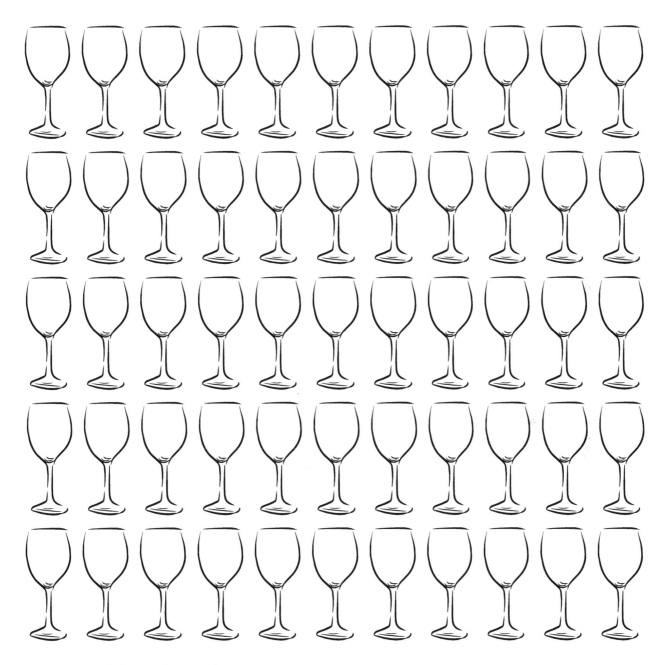

How long did it take you? _____

LICE CHECK!!

Connect the nits to reveal the hidden message.

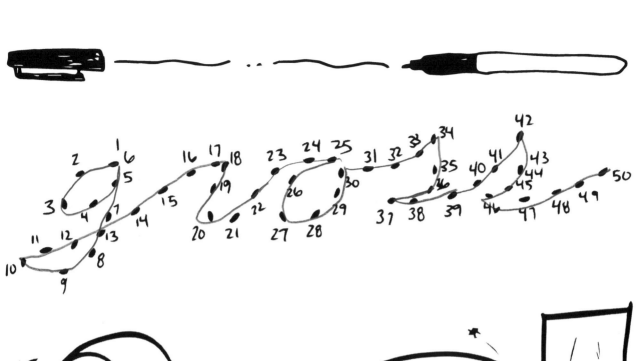

CRAYON CRAZINESS

What color does a staff meeting mean to you?

Early Release

School's Out!

Sunday Funday

Back to School

Detention

Extra Credit

Wine O'Clock

Late Homework

Lamination Station

Target Bill

Staff Meeting

Listening Ears

Bathroom Break

Lesson Planning

DIZZY doodles

Turn these wine glass stains into a work of art. Doodle to your hard-working heart's content!

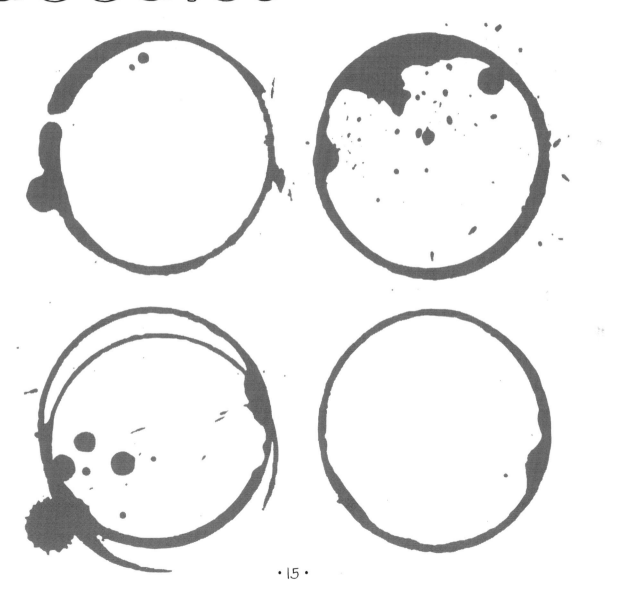

WHO IS IT TODAY?

Color in your least favorite student.
It's okay to color in more than one!

the
Tattle-Tale

the
Whiner

the Booger
Eater

the Bully

WHAT IS IN YOUR BROWN BAG?

List the items you WISH you could have in your lunch! Decorate to discourage prying eyes in the teacher's lounge.

_____

_____

_____

_____

_____

_____

_____

HOT SINGLE DAD
CONFERENCE ALERT!

What should you wear?

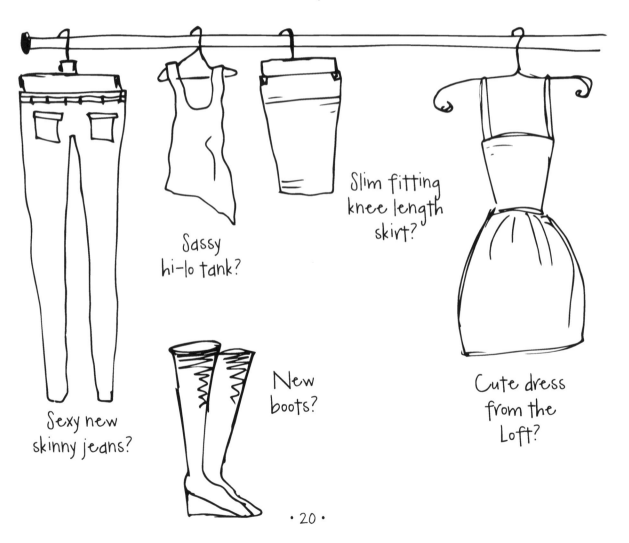

Sassy
hi-lo tank?

Slim fitting
knee length
skirt?

Sexy new
skinny jeans?

New
boots?

Cute dress
from the
Loft?

Draw and color an outfit that will keep him engaged in
your "core curriculum." Shopping trip anyone?

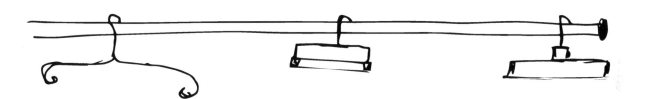

THEY SAID WHAAAAT?!?!

Never forget those precious gems!
Archive your favorites for posterity.

LIQUIDS TO USE LIBERALLY!

Create your own liquid hierarchy by ranking these essential liquids in order of importance from 1-6.

Coffee _____

Cocktail _____

Lysol _____

Hand Sanitizer _____

Glue _____

Diet Soda _____

NOT ALL WHO WANDER ARE LOST...

Some just need a tan and a cocktail. Find the quickest way to your summer vacation.

WHEN YOUR PRINCIPAL IS TALKING BUT ALL YOU CAN THINK ABOUT IS THE BOX OF DONUTS IN THE BREAKROOM.

STOP WITH THE "VERY"!!!

Soothe your soul and find a better alternative with some vivacious vocab!

ACROSS

3. VERY confused
5. VERY busy
8. VERY afraid
9. VERY dry
11. VERY angry
14. VERY cold
15. VERY cheap

DOWN

1. VERY excited
2. VERY big
4. VERY annoying
6. VERY bad
7. VERY easy
10. VERY dangerous
12. VERY calm
13. VERY colorful

Answers on page 93.

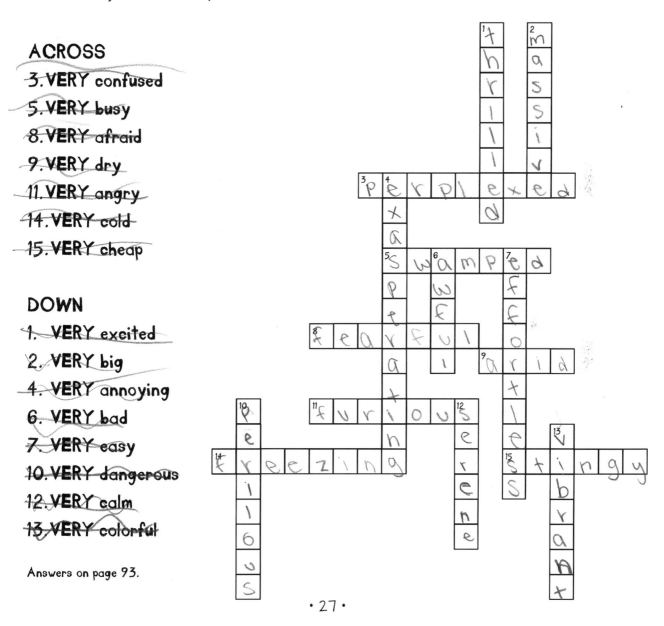

WHAT WOULD YOU REALLY SAY?
TO THE HELICOPTER MOM

We know you really can't, but what if you totally could?!

TEACHING IS MY JAM!

Doodle some "special" ingredients you would put in your teaching jam.
Examples: wine, chocolate, Adderall.

PENCIL PROBLEMS

Match the month to the pencil that reflects your level of desperation as the year wears on.

August   October   December

February   April   June

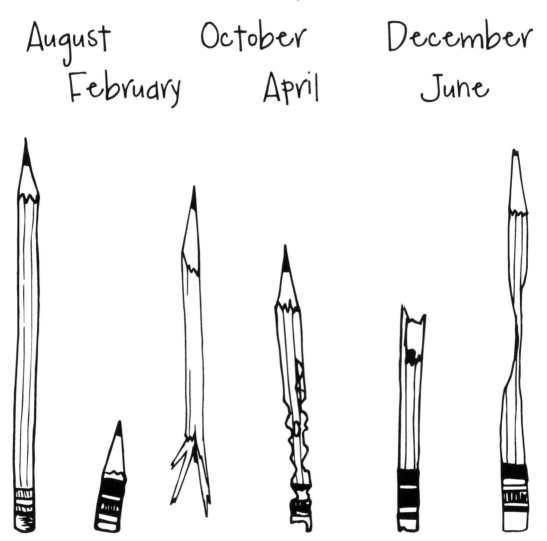

CRAFTY CONSEQUENCES...

this girl is going down. Concoct your retribution.

_____

_____

_____

_____

_____

_____

GET YOUR DOODLE ON...

Only Monday afternoon and already wishing for Friday?
Doodle some delicious goodies for the table in the teacher lounge.

ARE YOU FEVER FREE?

Who came in with what today? Do you know your germs?
Match 'em up!

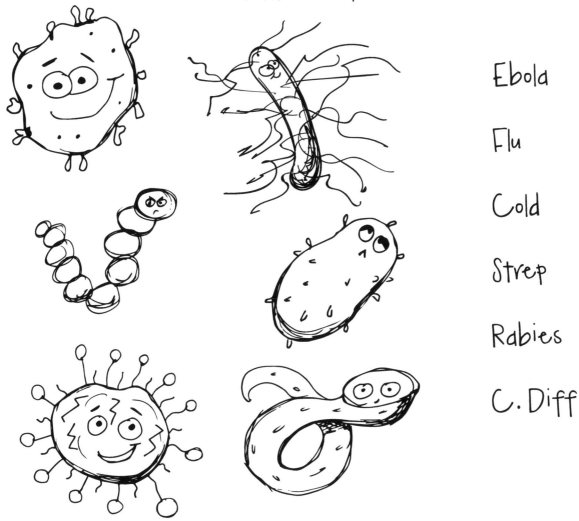

Ebola

Flu

Cold

Strep

Rabies

C. Diff

Answers on page 94.

TGIF DINNER

You survived another week!
Celebrate with carbs and a love note to self.

You Made It!

POUR YOURSELF SOME PEACE.

Escape the school week – it's time to treat yourself to a glass...or three.

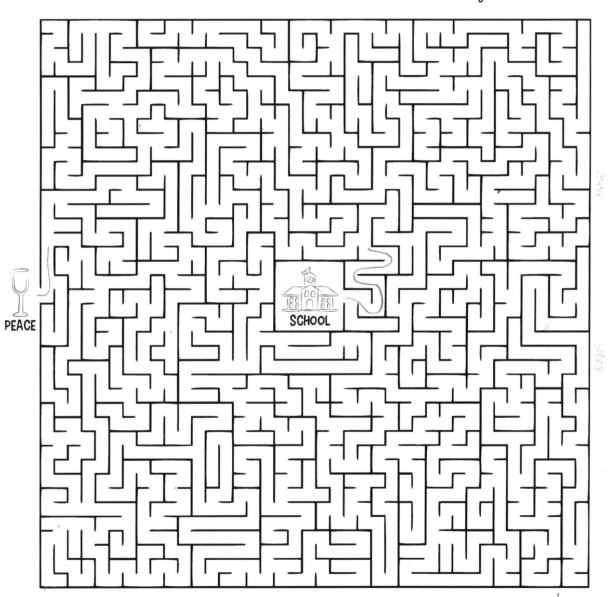

TGIF ANYONE?

Color in your favorite day of the week.

Monday

Tuesday

Wednesday

Thursday

Vodka

Friday.

NO MONEY.

NO MONEY.

NO MONEY.

NO MONEY.

NO MONEY.

NO MONEY.

NO MONEY.

WHAT WOULD YOU REALLY SAY?
TO YOUR ASSISTANT

We know you really can't, but what if you totally could?!

GET YOUR DOODLE ON...

turn these shapes into your adorable little blockheads!

YOU'RE STRANDED ON A DESERTED ISLAND...

You will die without what?

Copier

Planner

Laminator

Coffee

KIDS ARE GROSS WORD SEARCH

```
E D X B D T S L R R D U
Y O B A L E T L O O A M
E O Y C O N S E T D B O
K L F K M J W M T O O L
N B X P X B I S E Y O R
I J O A O X P K N D G X
P O R C B V E C A O E A
G B H K H O G O P B R G
F Z A C C M T S P D S L
I H E H N I H E L S I P
D F V E U T F L E C H E
G T V E L T M A E A Q R
E Y L S T S Y T C H A T
T J U E M I L S M W B S
```

backpack cheese
blood
body odor
boogers
fidget
goop
lice
lunch box mold
pink eye
rotten apple
slime
stale sock smell
strep
vomit
wipe

WHAT DOESN'T BELONG?

Find the nine items that have no business on a playground.

Answers on page 92.

BEST SELLERS

Jot down some titles of future bestsellers you could write from your unique teaching experiences.

Your Child Isn't Bored...Your Child Just Sucks

101 Reasons it Doesn't Matter Who is First in Line

WHAT WOULD YOU REALLY SAY?
TO THE JANITOR
We know you really can't, but what if you totally could?!

WHAT WOULD YOU REALLY SAY?
TO YOUR FAVORITE BUDDY

We know you really can't, but what if you totally could?!

BOTTOMS UP! WEEKEND IS A 'COMIN!

```
C L X W S A O I Z D P K
Q O I E T Z N B S W I B
A K S Z E I Y A U V N I
X T Q M T F N O O I A R
T E I R O G F D C A C I
L E A R R P K O R T O U
M M Q I A A O E C I L Q
S R A U T G E L E A A I
G I N O I B R Z I M D A
F R N V D L V A Y T A D
C I L P N T A P M G A U
C R E D W I N E U I X N
N O B R U O B M A W N B
C J G E N I W E T I H W
```

beer
pina colada
cosmopolitan
mai tai
tequila
vodka tonic
daiquiri
bourbon
margarita
red wine
white wine
coffee
gin
martini
sangria

WHAT WOULD YOU REALLY SAY?
TO THE CLASS DIVA

We know you really can't, but what if you totally could?!

THE WAIT IS FINALLY OVER!

It is 7:00 p.m. and no one stands between you and the copier!

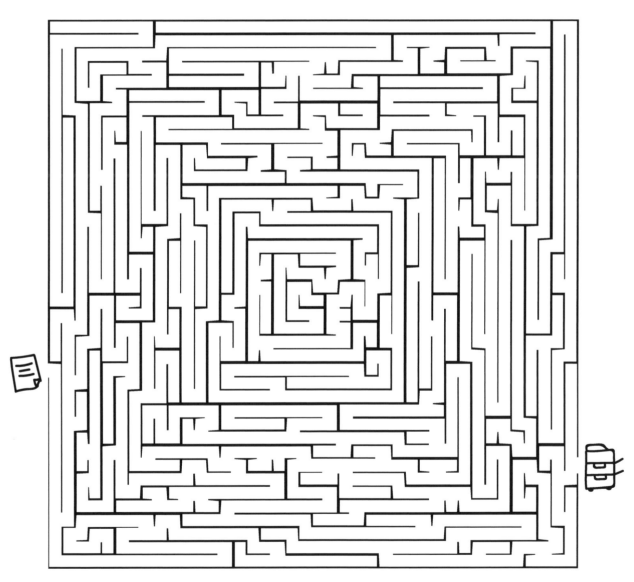

COME AGAIN???

Students aren't the only ones who can't shut their traps.
Write down your favorite parental one-liners.

TIME FOR A LITTLE DIPLOMACY!

Sometimes teachers have to be "diplomatic" in how they express their thoughts.
Match the sentiments or risk losing your job!

Your child is quite a character.

Your child has such an appetite for life!

Every child is a gift.

It's probably time to start to talk about personal hygiene.

Your child has amazing language skills!

We ask that every child stay seated during assembly.

Your child has a very strong personality.

I appreciate your input.

Apple doesn't fall far...

Let me do my job.

Do you have any plans to move?

Your child likes to eat dirt.

They never shut up.

If I have the receipt, can I return them?

They don't let me use duct tape.

Your kid stinks.

Answers on page 95.

SAID IS DEAD.

Be the thesaurus that you know you are.

ACROSS

5. loud!

8. ask nicely

11. complaining students

12. hahahaha

13. asked without manners

15. bossy pants

DOWN

1. in your head?

2. not serious

3. "We..we..we.."

4. come again?

6. loud

7. more complaining students

9. in your head

10. sadly

11.

14. in response to a question

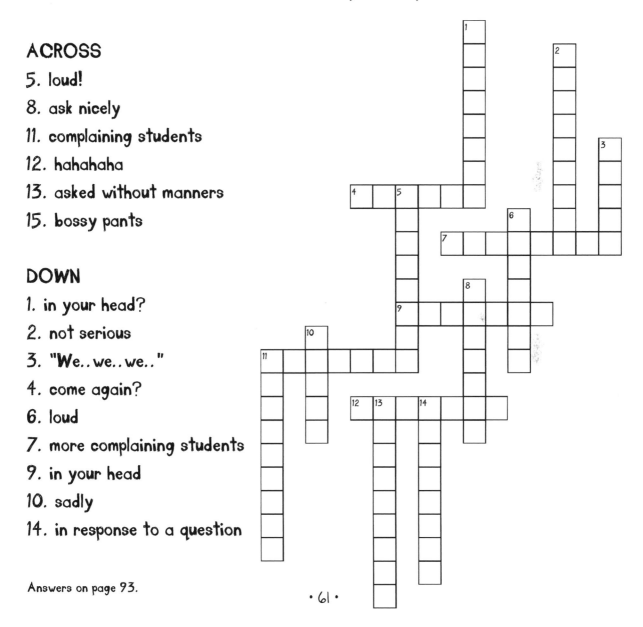

Answers on page 93.

ARE YOU FLUENT IN EMOJI?

Seems like everything can be expressed in a simple icon these days.
Prove your prowess.

innocent

lovestruck

arrogant

bored

exasperated

hungover

meditative

pained

smug

wasted

withdrawn

indifferent

Answers on page 93.

BACK TO SCHOOL SUPPLIES!

```
I  P  J  L  I  K  O  O  B  L  S  S
K  X  L  P  I  W  M  J  Z  I  H  H
E  C  A  A  S  C  H  S  F  Q  A  A
L  D  I  L  N  N  N  K  S  U  R  R
S  A  P  T  K  N  S  E  S  O  P  E
V  N  P  L  S  T  E  R  P  R  I  S
O  J  E  T  A  E  O  R  E  R  E  A
L  E  V  P  O  S  U  D  H  A  W  R
X  C  L  I  S  P  N  L  K  D  H  E
Y  E  B  I  Q  I  R  W  G  N  L  R
R  L  C  H  B  G  E  L  G  E  U  I
T  S  E  L  P  A  T  S  A  L  R  J
N  O  T  E  B  O  O  K  U  A  Y  C
C  R  A  Y  O  N  V  M  U  C  B  S
```

binder
crayon
laptop
pencil
sharpie
liquor
book
eraser
planner
calendar
ipad
notebook
scissors
staples
stapler
gluestick
pens

GET YOUR DOODLE ON...

When is that bell going to ring?
Pass the time by doodling the strangest things you secretly want to laminate.

WHO GAVE OUT THIS NUMBER?

Has your number tragically leaked out into the community?
What crazy things are people texting you now?!

THINGS I'M TIRED OF SAYING!!!

```
S  N  W  Q  S  J  D  X  E  L  Y  D
H  A  L  U  E  P  K  K  H  C  P  O
O  L  O  I  R  L  R  S  T  I  G  N
W  P  O  E  E  M  O  E  K  Z  T  T
Y  N  H  T  N  A  W  D  C  I  Y  I
O  O  C  P  I  K  E  R  I  B  H  N
U  S  S  L  T  E  M  U  L  R  E  T
R  S  O  E  Y  C  O  O  T  W  S  E
W  E  T  A  N  O  H  Y  N  D  A  R
O  L  K  S  O  P  F  N  O  N  S  R
R  O  C  E  W  I  V  A  D  B  V  U
K  A  A  F  Z  E  J  E  D  E  L  P
B  U  B  C  F  S  K  L  Y  E  L  T
N  W  O  D  S  L  I  C  N  E  P  M
```

back to school
don't lick the
make copies
serenity now
clean your desk
homework
pencils down
show your work
don't interrupt
lesson plan
quiet please

GET YOUR DOODLE ON...

Lesson planning writer's block?
Doodle some outrageous lesson plan ideas that your principal would totes veto.

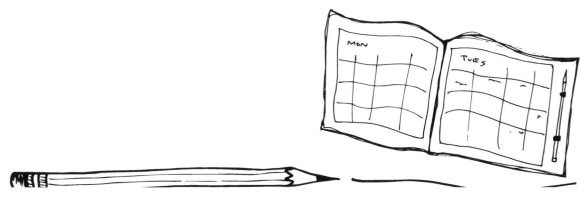

NAME THAT ALLERGEN!

Because these days...EVERYONE'S allergic!

Answers on page 94.

IT'S WRONG TO LABEL KIDS!

Or is it?

```
S  A  E  K  T  D  M  W  W  N  N  K
D  T  E  Z  V  U  E  K  D  P  I  T
B  E  N  P  R  I  N  C  E  S  S  E
G  O  N  A  R  S  A  O  X  D  X  P
C  J  O  D  P  Q  W  J  Q  O  R  S
R  P  O  K  M  Y  R  Q  B  R  U  R
Y  F  U  K  W  V  T  R  G  K  Q  E
B  W  N  N  Y  O  E  R  M  T  S  H
A  K  K  D  K  T  R  K  A  W  S  C
B  Y  I  M  T  M  A  M  I  M  Q  A
Y  V  L  A  P  U  K  C  U  S  S  E
A  H  H  L  N  E  R  D  A  I  X  T
S  C  Z  W  U  F  I  C  X  Z  P  T
B  P  O  M  Z  B  Q  R  Y  O  K  V
```

bookworm

cry baby

geek

princess

suck up

bully

diva

jock

punk

teacher's pet

chatterbox

dork

nerd

smartypants

weirdo

CARPOOL CRAZINESS!!!

Does anyone like carpool duty? Doodle some of the worst drivers in line.

Why aren't these kids on the bus?

KNOW YOUR GNATS!

Kids are gross...bugs are grosser! Who's crawling in your classroom?

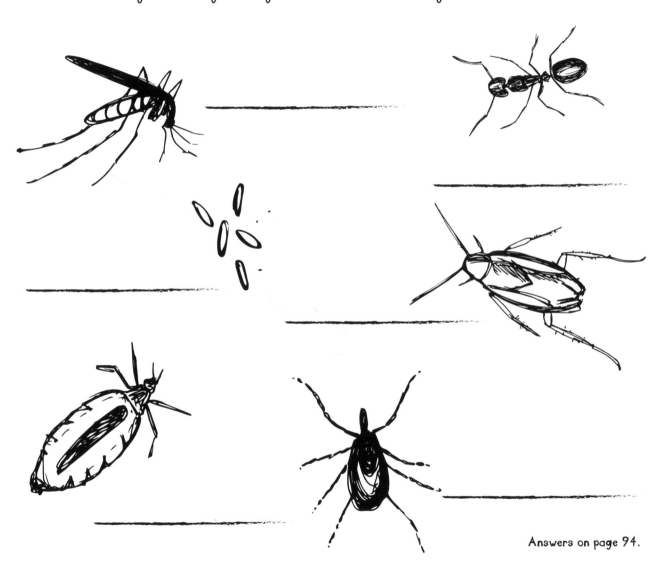

Answers on page 94.

YOU'RE STRANDED ON A DESERTED ISLAND...

Who are you least likely to murder before help arrives?

Cocky Kid

Helicopter Mom

the Whiner

Booger Eater

Shy Guy

the Bully

Diva

WHAT'S THAT SMELL?

Doodle some characters that you might find swimming
around in today's mystery lunch special.

WHAT WOULD YOU REALLY SAY?
TO THE BULLY

We know you really can't, but what if you totally could?!

TEACHERS NEED LOVE, LIQUOR...
and their own emojis!

principal observation

parent conference

inside recess

back to school

classroom set up

last day of school

summer

standardized test day

just tired

lesson planning done

carpool duty

running into students
at the store

Answers on page 93.

GET YOUR DOODLE ON...

Flexible seating anyone?
Kids don't need chairs...if you have Pinterest.

WHAT DOESN'T BELONG?

Something is amiss here... circle the items that might not be suitable for school.

Answers on page 92.

SILENCE PLEASE!

How many ways can you say SHUT UP? Without, you know, saying SHUT UP.

1. _____
2. _____
3. _____
4. _____
5. _____
6. _____
7. _____
8. _____
9. _____
10. _____
11. _____
12. _____
13. _____
14. _____
15. _____
16. _____

Answers on page 95.

WHAT WOULD YOU REALLY SAY?
TO THE HOT SINGLE DAD
We know you really can't, but what if you totally could?!

WHAT WOULD YOU REALLY SAY?
TO YOUR INCOMPETENT COLLEAGUE
We know you really can't, but what if you totally could?!

WHAT IS YOUR JAM?

What is your favorite Monday morning playlist to psych yourself up to survive just one more day.

_____

_____

_____

_____

_____

_____

_____

ABOUT
KAREN CAMPBELL

Karen Campbell is a full time artist and owner of Awesome Art School which is (as it's name suggests) an awesome art school! She is also the author of the *How to Draw Fun Fab Faces Series* (available on Amazon). When she is not slinging paint and drawing characters she is parenting her crazy handsome boys with her partner in crime, her husband Sean.

To learn all about Karen and her ongoing artful adventures, please visit www.karencampbellartist.com. See videos of the artist at work: youtube.com/coolmamacraftsapex. To enroll in free online classes visit: awesomeartschool.com

ABOUT
KRIS TAFT MILLER

Kris is a graphic designer, a former teacher, and a mom! She owns KT Design, LLC and does web design, logo design, book design and more. She worked at Disney animation for a decade (cool..right?) before this awesome dude, Jeremy, lured her across the country to North Carolina where she began her freelancing company. Her wildly popular and clever teaching printables can be found on her website. Check out Kris's store and portfolio at the links below.

Her favorite thing to do is lounge on the lake with her two gorgeous boys, Charlie and James and her awesome husband, Jeremy.

(FUN) www.printdesignsbykris.com
(Corporate) www.ktdesignllc.com

CONNECT SOCIALLY...

TO KAREN:

- karencampbellartist.com
- facebook.com/karencampbellartist
- instagram.com/karencampbellartist
- coolmamacrafts.etsy.com
- youtube.com/coolmamacraftsapex
- awesomeartschool.com

TO KRIS:

- printdesignsbykris.com
- facebook.com/teachcreatively
- instagram.com/printdesignsbykris
- printdesignsbykris.etsy.com
- teacherspayteachers.com/Store/Print-Designs-By-Kris

ALL THE ANSWERS!

Not to all of life's questions, just the puzzles in this book.
Don't cheat, what kind of an exmaple is that setting?

WHAT DOESN'T BELONG?
PAGE 82

snake

hot coffee

rat

snake

snake

booby graffiti

Tinder 4 Dummies

cocktail book

BAD KIDS
not nice

liquor

eye chart

WHAT DOESN'T BELONG?
PAGE 41

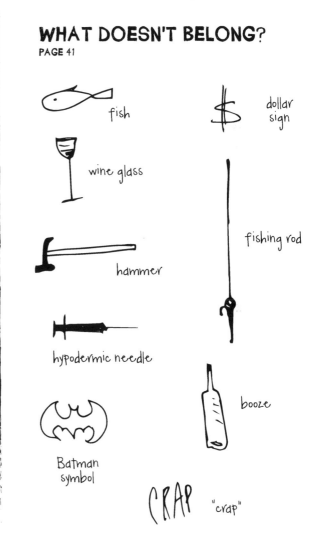

fish

dollar sign

wine glass

fishing rod

hammer

hypodermic needle

booze

Batman symbol

CRAP "crap"

VERY
CROSSWORD PUZZLE
PAGE 27

ACROSS
3. perplexed
5. swamped
8. fearful
9. arid
11. furious
14. freezing
15. stingy

DOWN
1. thrilled
2. massive
4. exasperating
6. awful
7. effortless
10. perilous
12. serene
13. vibrant

SAID
CROSSWORD PUZZLE
PAGE 55

ACROSS
5. exclaimed
8. requested
11. groaned
12. laughed
13. demanded
15. insisted

DOWN
1. wondered
2. joked
3. stammered
4. mumbled
6. shouted
7. whined
9. thought
10. cried
14. answered

MATCH THE EMOJI
PAGE 62

innocent
lovestruck
arrogant
bored
exasperated
hungover
meditative
pained
smug
wasted
withdrawn
indifferent

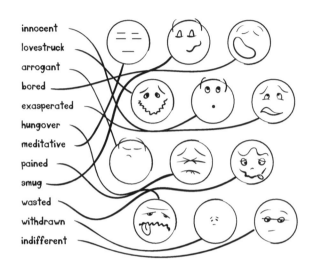

MATCH THE TEACHER EMOJI
PAGE 80

principal observation
parent conference
inside recess
back to school
classroom set up
last day of school
summer
standardized test day
just tired
lesson planning done
carpool duty
running into students
at the store

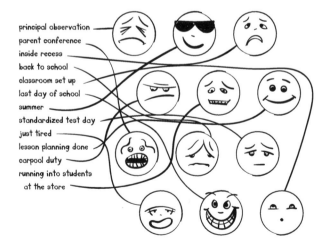

NAME THAT ALLERGEN
PAGE 70

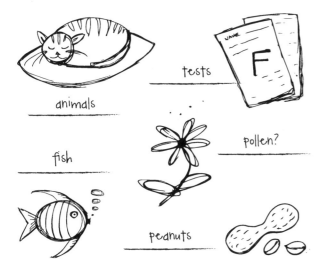
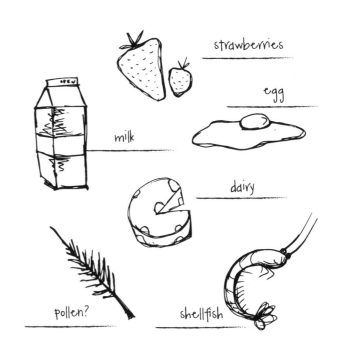

animals

tests

fish

pollen?

peanuts

strawberries

egg

milk

dairy

pollen?

shellfish

NAME THAT GNAT
PAGE 76

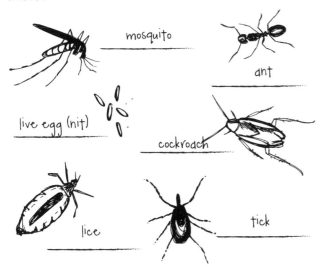

mosquito

ant

live egg (nit)

cockroach

lice

tick

NAME THAT VIRUS
PAGE 32

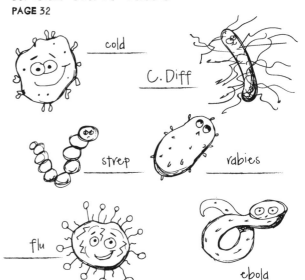

cold

C. Diff

strep

rabies

flu

ebola

SPILL COLOR BY NUMBER

PAGE 8

1. Blood
2. Vomit
3. Bubble Gum
4. Slime
5. Glue
6. Boogers
7. Urine

SILENCE PLEASE

PAGE 84

1. Shhhhhhh
2. Silence!
3. Hold your tongue
4. Shush!
5. Stop talking.
6. Quit chattering.
7. Zip it.
8. Pipe down.
9. Shut it.
10. Zip your lips.
11. Button it.
12. Put a sock in it.
13. Lips sealed.
14. Quiet down.
15. Hush!
16. Shut your trap.

THINGS WE SAY

PAGE 59

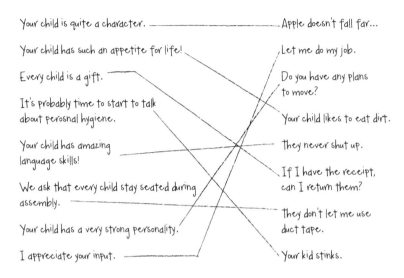

Your child is quite a character. — Apple doesn't fall far...

Your child has such an appetite for life! — Let me do my job.

Every child is a gift. — Do you have any plans to move?

It's probably time to start to talk about perosnal hygiene. — Your child likes to eat dirt.

Your child has amazing language skills! — they never shut up.

We ask that every child stay seated during assembly. — If I have the receipt, can I return them?

Your child has a very strong personality. — they don't let me use duct tape.

I appreciate your input. — Your kid stinks.

Made in the USA
Columbia, SC
03 December 2017